£8.95 VOCAL / PIANO

LEONA LEWIS
SPIRIT

Exclusive distributors:

Music Sales Limited
14-15 Berners Street, London W1T 3LJ, UK.

Music Sales Pty Limited
120 Rothschild Avenue, Rosebery, NSW 2018, Australia.

Order No. AM993080   ISBN 978-1-84772-494-6
This book © Copyright 2007 by Wise Publications, a division of Music Sales Limited.

Music arranged by Derek Jones.
Music processed by Paul Ewers Music Design.
Edited by Fiona Bolton.
Cover photograph by Ralph Mecke.
Printed in the EU.

www.musicsales.com

Wise Publications
part of The Music Sales Group

London / New York / Paris / Sydney / Copenhagen / Berlin / Madrid / Tokyo

BLEEDING LOVE

Words & Music by Jesse McCartney & Ryan Tedder

To Coda ⊕

You cut me o - pen,____

ooh._____

2. Try-ing hard not to hear   but they talk so loud,

their pierc-ing sounds fill my ears,   try to fill me with doubt,   yet I know that the

goal   is to keep me from fall - ing,____   hey,_____ yeah.____

5

find it hard to be-lieve, I'll be wear-ing these scars for ev-

-'ry-one to see. I don't care what they say, I'm in love with you.

They try to pull me a-way, but they don't know the truth. My heart's crip-pled by the

vein that I keep on clos-ing. Ooh, you cut me o-pen and I

WHATEVER IT TAKES

Words & Music by Leona Lewis, Alonzo Stevenson & Tony Reyes

(Da da da da da da. Da da da da da da da. Da da da da da da. Da da da da da da da.)

1. Peo- ple say___ love comes and goes,___ but they don't un- der-stand what they

HOMELESS

Words & Music by Jörgen Elofsson

va-can-cies,__ just emp-ti-ness. With-out your love__ I'm home-less..

With-out your love__ I'm home-less._____

Oh!_____ Oh, my ba - by, I'm

sor - ry,___ sor - ry_____ that you don't love me an - y -

BETTER IN TIME

Words & Music by Andrea Martin & Jonathan Rotem

Original key F♯ major

1. It's been the long-est win-ter with-out you.
2. I could-n't turn on the T.V.

I did-n't know where to turn___ to.___
with-out some-thing there to re-mind___ me.___

See, some-how I can't for-get___ you,___
Was it all that eas - y___

af - ter all that we've been___ through.___
to just put a - side your feel - ings?___

Go - ing, com - ing, thought I heard a knock. Who's there? No - one. Think-ing that
If I'm dream - ing, don't wan-na laugh. Hurt my feel - ings, but that's the path

19

it's time I let you go___ so I___ can be free.___

And live my life___ how it___ should be.___

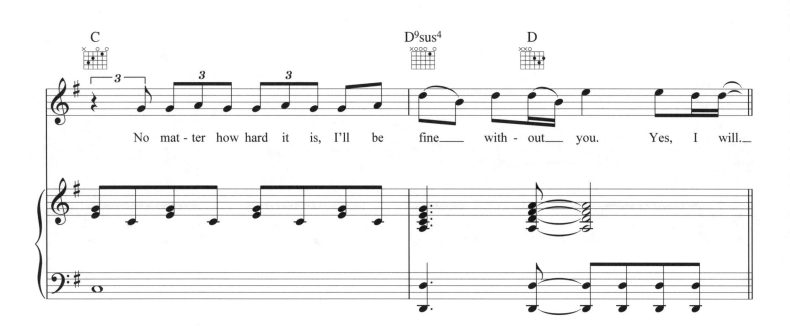

No mat-ter how hard it is, I'll be fine___ with-out___ you. Yes, I will.___

YESTERDAY

Words & Music by Louis Biancaniello, Sam Watters,
Nina Woodford, Jordan Omley & Michael Mani

1. I just can't be-lieve you're gone,_____ still wait-ing for morn-ing to come.__
2. You al-ways used to say,_____ I should be thank-ful for ev - e -ry day.__

I can still find the strength_ in the mo-ments we made._____ I'm look-ing

back on yes-ter-day.____ They can take to-mor-row and the plans we made._

They can take the mu-sic that we'll nev-er play._ All the bro - ken dreams,_ take ev-'ry thing. Just

take it a-way, but they can nev-er have yes-ter-day. They can take the fu-ture that we'll nev-er know._

TAKE A BOW

Words & Music by Louis Biancaniello,
Sam Watters, Wayne Wilkins & Ryan Tedder

I WILL BE

Words & Music by Avril Lavigne,
Max Martin & Lukasz Gottwald

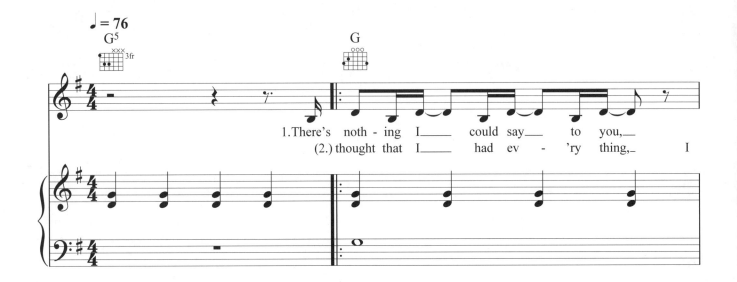

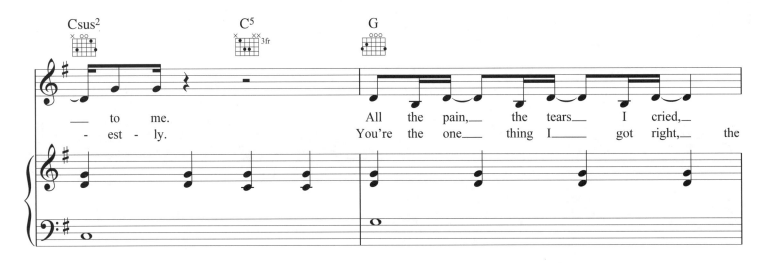

ANGEL

Words & Music by Mikkel Eriksen,
Tor Erik Hermansen & Johnta Austin

noth-ing's big e-nough to hide_ us.
prom - ise of to - mor - row.
When we make love it's o - ver-whelm-ing.

I just touch the heav - ens. You're_ an an - gel._____ You're_ an an-

- gel._____ I said this world, this world could

leave us an - y day._____ But my love for you, it will

43

never go a-way.___ And I___ don't wan-na go to sleep___ 'cause you are like a dream.___ For ev-'ry night I say___ a prayer,___ well, I___ swear you are___ the ans - wer. You're___ an an - gel.___ You're___ an an -

To Coda

1.
- gel.___ You're___ an an - gel.___ 2. So we take___ each

44

HERE I AM

Words & Music by Walter Afanasieff,
Leona Lewis & Brett Cornelius

heal - er for___ your pain,___ I will be___ there time___ and time___ a - gain.___

When you need some - one___ to love___ you,___ here I am.

Vocal ad lib.

2. If you have need some - one___ to love___ you, here I am.___

Oh. Ev-'ry-bod-y needs some-bod — y who they can pour their heart and soul in - to. If you need a

I'M YOU

Words & Music by Shaffer Smith & Eric Hudson

are   you   gon - na   take___   it?_____
2. Oh,   you're   not   cra - zy.

Look   in   my   eyes,___   help   me   make___   this   make___
They   fin - 'lly   re - al - ised   that   you   and   I   is   all   the   help___   you   need.___

___   sense.___   Night   af - ter   night___   you   sat   up   and   cried,___
_____   So   why   are   we   sit - ting   here   on   the   floor?___

___   won - d'rin   when   you're   gon - na   see   this   clear - er.   You   don't   e - ven   re -
___   We   ain't   cry - ing   no   more.___   I   am___   your   soul,

THE BEST YOU NEVER HAD

Words & Music by Billy Steinberg & Joshua Berman

THE FIRST TIME EVER I SAW YOUR FACE

Words & Music by Ewan MacColl

69

FOOTPRINTS IN THE SAND

Words & Music by Per Magnusson,
David Kreuger, Richard Page & Simon Cowell

73

A MOMENT LIKE THIS

Words & Music by Jörgen Elofsson & John Reid

80

123456789